This bite-sized book has been designed to offer some useful tips to help boost your mood. It will help you to achieve the following:

- Build a toolkit of easy-to-apply mood boosters
- Support your mental health in challenging times
- Choose and embrace healthy coping mechanisms
- Manage stress levels and feel more energised
- Look on the brighter side of life and feel better

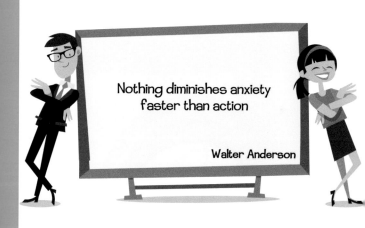

Nothing diminishes anxiety
faster than action

Walter Anderson

How to
boost your
mood

Little by little does the trick

Aesop

Take the first step

When you feel stressed, anxious or overwhelmed, it can be so difficult to know what to do next. Identifying and taking one small step towards doing something positive will help to diminish anxiety. It doesn't have to be a big effort, just something small.

Once you take the first micro step, the next one will be easier and before you know it, you will start to feel a little better and a little brighter. There is a saying that originates from a famous Chinese proverb: "A journey of a thousand miles begins with a single step". Let your journey begin one small step at a time.

Your day will go the way the corners of your mouth turn

Smile

This may seem like a basic thing to do. However, the simple act of smiling can give you a real boost. Smiling stimulates neural messaging in your brain which helps to elevate your mood. A smile can trigger the release of mood-boosting neurotransmitters like dopamine and serotonin.

When you look in the mirror first thing in the morning, take a moment to pause and smile at your reflection. Start your day the way that you want it to continue. Remember that life is like a mirror, smile at it and it smiles back at you.

Get some fresh air

Exercise is highly beneficial for our mental health and overall mood. Even on a cold day, it is so important to wrap up and go for an energising walk. Even if you only walk around the block, it will make you feel so much better. Breathing in fresh air and absorbing natural daylight is especially important in the winter months. The cooler weather is great for invigorating and stimulating the senses.

With so many more people now working from home, it could be easy to stay indoors all day which isn't healthy. So, set yourself a goal to get outside and breathe in some fresh air, at the very least once a day.

Stretch

Stretching is an excellent mood-boosting activity. Apart from the physiological benefits, such as increased flexibility and the reduced chance of injury, stretching has other benefits too. It helps release neurochemicals in the brain, like serotonin, which is the primary chemical associated with joy and elation.

When you are sitting at your desk, make a point of standing up every thirty minutes and stretch. Even if you only do it for a couple of minutes, it will make you feel great.

Everything has beauty,
but not everyone sees it

Confucius

Connect with nature

An increasing amount of studies show that our levels of productivity and sense of well-being improve when we connect with nature. Exposure to natural sensory experiences such as the sound of running water, the smell of flowers or freshly cut grass can reduce stress and relax the mind.

It is worth noting that some houseplants can have health benefits. For example 'Peace Lilies' have been proven to combat harmful household chemicals and are also highly effective at removing mould spores from the air. Essentially, they are an organic air purifier that can make you feel more comfortable, especially if you are now finding yourself working from home.

If there is magic on this planet,
it is contained in water

Loren Eiseley

Keep Hydrated

Dehydration can affect your emotions because it slows your circulation, which lowers blood flow. This means less oxygen travels to your brain and it is not able to function properly. If you find yourself feeling irritated, nervous, sluggish, or even hungry, you may well be dehydrated.

By keeping hydrated, you will feel more alert and energised. There are lots of delicious herbal teas available and these will also add to your recommended quota of around 6-8 glasses a day. Chopping up your favourite fruit and adding it to water can make it taste more delicious. A good way to boost your fluid intake is to drink a glass of water before you eat a meal and always keep a topped-up reusable bottle with you. This will help you to keep hydrated throughout the day.

Eat "good mood" food

If you are feeling low, make a conscious effort to have a healthy day. Avoid foods which make your blood sugar rise and fall rapidly, such as sweets, biscuits, sugary drinks, and alcohol. Eat lots of things you know will boost your energy and eliminate all the toxins.

Chop up some fruit and vegetables and keep them in the fridge to snack on. If you are looking for a quick energy boost, try a handful of pumpkin seeds, a couple of brazil nuts and a small piece of dark chocolate. This is a much more nutritious treat than a refined sugary snack.

Smell your way to a good mood

Because smell plays such an important role in memory, mood and emotion, oil diffusers can be helpful with lifting and calming our mood. Diffusers disperse essential oils as a fine vapour through the air so they can be absorbed gently into the body through your respiratory system. The aromas from the essential oils can also encourage the nervous system to transmit signals to the limbic system in the brain which handles emotion.

Some of the best essential oils for relaxation include: lavender, rose, ylang-ylang, bergamot, chamomile, jasmine and cedarwood. The smell of citrus can boost your body's production of serotonin, the hormone that makes you feel happy. Lemon scent is regarded to be the most powerful of the citrus smells and can increase mental stimulation.

Replace caffeine with herbal teas

Too much caffeine can cause nervousness, agitation, rapid or irregular heartbeat, dizziness, and mood fluctuations. Caffeine can also increase the body's levels of cortisol, the "stress hormone," which can lead to moodiness. Caffeine increases dopamine levels in your system and can give you an immediate surge of energy. This may well boost you at first. However, after it wears off, you can end up feeling low.

Sipping something more soothing can also give you an opportunity to slow down and savour the present moment. There are so many delicious flavours available and herbal teas are a healthy alternative to caffeinated drinks.

Smarten yourself up

Although it may feel like a huge effort sometimes to get dressed up, it will be worthwhile because when you look in the mirror it will give you a boost. We all feel better when we smarten ourselves up.

Working from home has become more the norm and it can be easy to fall into bad habits. Roaming about in your pyjamas or dressing gown may be the easiest option. However, it won't help you feel energised. The best thing to do is to get up, get ready and take a pride in your appearance.

Wear some bright coloured clothes

Various research suggests that wearing brighter clothes can make you happier. Bright colours trigger responses in the brain that can release hormones associated with happiness.

Looking at bright colours releases dopamine, which makes us feel happier. So, you can get a boost by simply putting on something bright and colourful. This is especially helpful during the drabber winter months where darker colours tend to be favoured.

Reach out and connect

Building and sustaining a strong network of supportive friends, family and work colleagues can really help during times of difficulty. It is important to have people in your life who you can trust and confide in. Research indicates that people with strong and broad social relationships are happier and healthier. Close relationships provide love, meaning and support, and enhance our self esteem.

Bottling things up can increase anxiety so it can really help to reach out and talk to a friend or family member who will listen to you. One of the best things about communication, in whatever form, is that it will help you to get a different perspective on what may be troubling you.

Laughter lets me relax. It's the equivalent of taking a deep breath, letting it out and saying, 'This, too, will pass'

Odette Pollar

Let the laughter in

Even in challenging times, it helps to seek out the funny side of situations. Having a good laugh can decrease stress hormones and increase immune cells and infection-fighting antibodies.

Laughter also triggers the release of endorphins, the body's natural feel-good chemicals, promoting an overall sense of well-being and relaxation. Endorphins can even temporarily relieve pain. So, whether it's watching your favourite comedian or connecting with someone who shares your sense of humour, find a way to let the laughter into your life.

How beautiful it is to do nothing,
and then to rest afterwards

Spanish Proverb

Practise mindfulness

The term mindfulness comes from Eastern spiritual and religious traditions. A great deal of scientific research now shows that the mindful approach to stress, anxiety and mental health is a helpful and increasingly popular way to deal with and diffuse high levels of stress.

Mindfulness refers to being completely in touch with, and aware of, the present moment and taking a non-evaluative and non-judgmental approach to your inner experience. It is essentially about creating intentional pauses, being present and noticing what is around you. There are lots of really good apps available and "Headspace" is one that comes highly recommended.

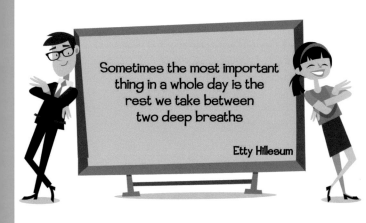

Sometimes the most important thing in a whole day is the rest we take between two deep breaths

Etty Hillesum

Focus on breathing

Breathing is one of the easiest forms of relaxation. If you are feeling stressed, focusing on your breathing can really help you to calm down. There are many simple breathing exercises that require no equipment and can be done anywhere.

Here is one example:

- Sit with your back straight and imagine a piece of string attached to the top of your head pulling you up.
- Close your eyes and focus on your breathing.
- Close your mouth and inhale through your nose to a mental count of four.
- Hold your breath for a count of four.
- Exhale completely through your mouth, slowly, to a count of eight.
- This is one breath. Now repeat six times.

List your proudest achievements

Make a list of three of your proudest and most positive accomplishments to remind yourself what you are capable of. This will give you an immediate boost of confidence.

When you are reviewing your list, take time to dwell upon the whole sensory experience you had when you achieved them. What did it feel like, look like, sound like? Transport yourself there and relive how good it felt and all the associated emotions will then boost you in the present moment.

Do a cons and pros list

A good way to release anxieties and worries is to write down what is bothering you. This will help you put them into perspective and tangibly take hold of what your concerns are. You can then work out how to flip them over into something more positive.

Start with the negatives/problems and then work out what the positives/opportunities could be. This a great way to exercise and reinforce solution-focused thinking.

Dance like nobody's watching;
love like you've never been hurt.
Sing like nobody's listening;
live like it's heaven on earth

Mark Twain

Listen to music and dance

Music can be so powerful with regards to stimulating emotions and research has demonstrated how music can be used as a therapeutic, mood-lifting solution to combat depression and anxiety. There are some great pieces of music that can make you feel better and singing along to songs with positive lyrics is a wonderful mood booster.

In addition, dancing about to your favourite track can be a great way to incorporate more physical activity into your day and is such fun.

Take a technoholiday

It is becoming increasingly obvious that our world is developing an unhealthy attachment to technology and mobile devices. Being constantly "switched on" is not good for your mental health. Various studies into neurological and emotional well-being highlight the need to take breaks.

Scanning social media can make you feel agitated, especially with all the news and unpleasant things that are shared so freely. Being selective about what you look at is important and establishing boundaries about how long you spend on your devices and setting time limits can be helpful.

Spend time around animals

Spending time around pets can help you to relax and feel calmer. When you stroke an animal, you release feel-good endorphins that help to reduce your heart rate. Playing with a pet also increases the levels of the feel-good chemicals serotonin and dopamine in your brain, which can help you feel happier.

According to a study, published in the Journal of Environmental Psychology, watching nature programmes can also boost your mood and reduce boredom levels from being indoors.

Sometimes all we need is a little pampering to help us feel better

Charles M. Schulz

Treat yourself

A little bit of pampering and treating yourself to something that you enjoy can be a great way to lift your spirits. This could be anything from cooking yourself a delicious meal, enjoying snuggling up in front of your favourite TV programme or just pottering about at home.

One way to pamper yourself is to take a relaxing soak in a bath. Warm water and bubble bath will loosen up your muscles and it's a great way to feel pampered without really doing a lot. Fifteen minutes soaking in a scented bath will help you feel relaxed and lighten your mind. Candles and calming music can be an additional way to luxuriate.

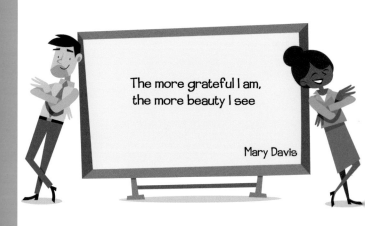

The more grateful I am,
the more beauty I see

Mary Davis

Take a daily dose of vitamin G

Vitamin G stands for "Vitamin Gratitude". Positive psychology research has identified that gratitude is strongly and consistently associated with happiness. Taking time daily to focus on things we are grateful for can help us to experience more positive emotions, improve our overall health, be more resilient and build stronger relationships.

So take time, every day, to think about things that you are grateful for in your life. Adopting an attitude of gratitude and gifting yourself a daily dose will help you to feel better and focus your mind in a more positive and appreciative way.

Be kind

When you are kind to yourself and to those around you, a hormone called oxytocin is released into your body and oxytocin triggers a release of nitric oxide. This chemical then dilutes your blood cells and shrinks inflammation in the cardiovascular system, which in turn reduces blood pressure and the chances of heart disease.

This is just one of the multiple benefits of kindness and, according to the Mental Health Foundation, helping others is beneficial for your own mental health and well-being. Being kind can also help to reduce stress.

So, for the very best mood booster of all, practise loving kindness.